Now you ca[n]
flute soloist
recorded arrangements

MOVIE HITS

TAKE THE LEAD

flute

IMP

International MUSIC Publications

International Music Publications Limited
Griffin House 161 Hammersmith Road London W6 8BS England

Series Editor: Sadie Cook

Editorial, production and recording: Artemis Music Limited
Design & Production: Space DPS Limited

Published 1999

International MUSIC Publications

International Music Publications Limited
Griffin House 161 Hammersmith Road London W6 8BS England

International Music Publications Limited

England: Griffin House
161 Hammersmith Road
London W6 8BS

Germany: Marstallstr. 8
D-80539 München

Denmark: Danmusik
Vognmagergade 7
DK1120 Copenhagen K

Italy: Via Campania 12
20098 San Giuliano Milanese
Milano

Spain: Magallanes 25
28015 Madrid

France: 20 Rue de la Ville-l'Eveque
75008 Paris

WARNER BROS. PUBLICATIONS U.S. INC.

USA: 15800 N.W. 48th Avenue
Miami, Florida 33014

Australia: 3 Talavera Road
North Ryde
New South Wales 2113

Scandinavia: P.O. Box 533
Vendevagen 85 B
S-182 15 Danderyd
Sweden

flute

TAKE THE LEAD

In the Book...

On the CD...

Because You Loved Me

(from *Up Close And Personal*)

Words and Music by Diane Warren

Demonstration   Backing

Blue Monday

(from *The Wedding Singer*)

Words and Music by
Stephen Morris, Peter Hook,
Bernard Sumner and Gillian Gilbert

Demonstration

Backing

Moderately fast

(Everything I Do) I Do It For You

(from *Robin Hood: Prince of Thieves*)

Words and Music by Bryan Adams,
Robert John 'Mutt' Lange and Michael Kamen

I Don't Want To Miss A Thing

(from *Armageddon*)

Demonstration

Backing

Words and Music by Diane Warren

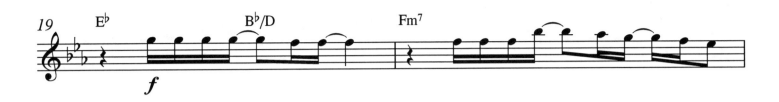

I Will Always Love You

(from *The Bodyguard*)

Words and Music by Dolly Parton

Demonstration   Backing

Star Wars (Main Title)

Demonstration

Backing

By John Williams

The Wind Beneath My Wings

(from *Beaches*)

Words and Music by
Larry Henley and Jeff Silbar

You Can Leave Your Hat On

(from *The Full Monty*)

Demonstration

Backing

Words and Music by Randy Newman

Moderate rock

7/99

Reproduced and printed by
Halstan & Co. Ltd., Amersham, Bucks., England